A little chicken can see a red robin in a bush.

The robin flaps his wings and he can fly in the sky.

The chicken flaps her wings. She flaps and flaps and flaps ...

... but she flops onto the grass. 'Oh, I can't fly,' she says.

The robin tells the chicken to run and flap her wings.

The chicken runs and flaps her wings, but she flops onto the grass.

‘Oh, I can’t fly,’ she says. ‘Chickens can’t fly. Bye, bye, robin.’

She runs away to play with all the other chickens who can't fly.